The Observation Hive

THE

OBSERVATION HIVE

KARL SHOWLER

*Technical Officer, the International
Bee Research Association*

BEE BOOKS NEW & OLD
STEVENTON, BASINGSTOKE, HANTS

To Muriel and Thomas Showler
who permitted my first observation
hive in their house roof

Printed in Great Britain by
Butler & Tanner Ltd, Frome and London

The chiefest cause, to read good bookes,
    That moves each studious minde
Is hope, some pleasure sweet therein,
    Or profit good to finde.
Now what delight can greater be
    Then secrets for to knowe,
Of Sacred Bees, the Muses Birds,
    All which this booke doth shew.
And if commodity thou crave,
    Learne here no little gaine
Of their most sweet and sov'raigne fruits,
    With no great cost or paine.
If pleasure then, or profit may
    To read induce thy minde;
In this smale Treatise choice of both
    Good Reader, thou shalt finde.

Charles Butler, *The Feminine Monarchie*, 1609

CONTENTS

Drawing a plan:
*Number of frames; Location: indoors or out; To rotate or not;
The hive body, windows and cover; Body; Windows; Shutters;
Cozy; Position of the entrance; Entrance tube; Feeder; Alight-
ing board*

ILLUSTRATIONS

LIST OF PHOTOGRAPHS

ix

LINE DRAWINGS

xi

ACKNOWLEDGEMENTS

This book was written at the request of John Kinross, of Bee Books New and Old, because no substantial publication on observation hives was available. I was encouraged by the Council and Director, Dr Eva Crane, of the International Bee Research Association, to pursue my special interest in observation hives.

During visits to beekeepers and beekeeping institutions, I have received much helpful advice and this is acknowledged with gratitude. Especial thanks must go to Dr Colin Butler and Dr John Free at the Rothamsted Experimental Station, for making their observation hives available for study. My wife, Betty Showler, took many of the photographs, and John Wade provided technical assistance in their preparation for use in this book. Mary King provided the delightful decorations used as chapter headings. Jean Corbett and Audrey Pitman prepared the manuscript for the printer.

Potters Barn   17 April 1978
Chalfont St Giles
Bucks

INTRODUCTION

Most people when they get the chance to stand in front of a honeybees' hive will be fascinated by the activity of these useful insects. The stream of foragers, many with coloured pollen loads on their legs; the young bees on orientation flights around the hive entrance; the noisy drones zooming to and fro, all create a scene which holds the onlooker spellbound until . . . the sudden sting; the guard bees attracted by the shadow of the visitor, the laden forager crashing into the unexpected blockage in its way, or the outward bound bee meeting up with a new obstruction on a once clear flight path. Whatever the cause, this unforeseen sting may well deter from further study the young naturalist or those not used to honeybees. In this little book I have tried to describe a number of ways in which the honeybee colony can be observed with safety, and without undue disturbance.

In addition to the casual use of observation hives, much of the current interest in their construction stems from the widening use of bees in education. A well planned and carefully stocked observation hive offers numerous opportunities for group study of the nest and habits of one of the most highly developed social insects. Observation hives permitted the elucidation of many problems facing beekeepers in the eighteenth and nineteenth centuries and even today play an important role in the scientific study of the honeybee. Many beekeepers, too, prepare this type of hive both for their own interest and as a feature at exhibitions and agricultural fairs.

Hives which allowed the undisturbed observation of the honeybee colony without prior manipulation were first described in the seventeenth century and, until the movable-comb hive became common, most observation hives contained small colonies with several fixed natural combs. Single 'unicomb' hives were developed in the nineteenth century and during its last quarter were very popular in the drawing-rooms of the gentry, and in competitive classes at honey shows.

1

Strangely, although there is a great deal of interest in observation hives, and certain hives have been described in some detail, no one has attempted to gather this information together; I hope *The Observation Hive* will go some way towards filling this gap in apicultural literature.

GENERAL CONSIDERATIONS

Whatever the objectives may be in the setting up of an observation hive the length of time for which the hive is required to be stocked is fundamental to its overall design and preparation. The permanent observation hive must be large enough for the bees to overwinter in it or at least survive prolonged periods of adverse weather; the semi-permanent one must permit the colony to be housed during the summer and transferred to alternative quarters during the winter; for short-term observation bees can be held for a few hours without undue difficulty, but within twenty-four hours they will need food, water and access to the open air in order to void on the wing.

There is also the general problem of temperature control. The ambient temperature surrounding smaller colonies may well fall so low as to make brood-rearing difficult; if too high it will make the combs too soft to support the weight of stores, nectar and brood. Population build-up in confined spaces also limits the natural development of the colony. Both these problems are discussed in the relevant sections but need to be considered at an early stage when planning the observation hive.

Observation hives, irrespective of the length of time they are to be maintained or their size, may be divided into two groups; those with several combs hanging side by side, the outer screening the middle ones from view—'multicomb' hives; and those with a single main range of comb—'unicomb' hives. The latter may well be subdivided by wooden frames which permit the range of comb to be dismantled and returned to a standard beehive.

Observation hives in a house or shed will not require the observer to wear a veil but, when they are located outdoors or it is wished to conduct observations at the entrance, children certainly should wear veils and reasonably bee-proof clothing. Observation hives located inside some type of casing may well receive sufficient jolting on opening to disturb the inmates and put the guard bees on the defensive.

3

CHAPTER ONE

MULTICOMB HIVES

ADAPTING A STANDARD MOVABLE-FRAME HIVE

The simplest way of obtaining some insight into the life of a colony is to provide windows in the crownboard and walls of a standard hive.

A glass or perspex crownboard will in a matter of moments allow the upper edges of the combs of a colony to be inspected. Spring assessments of a colony's growth, and in summer the sealing of stores can be made without difficulty. Regular notes on the bees' activity or lack of it can be made at all times of the year. Standard wooden crown or cover boards can be modified by the removal of part of the wooden panelling and the substitution of glass or perspex. If condensation on the glass is a problem the feed hole or Porter escape hole will provide some ventilation and secondary ventilation may be given at the edges by a row of small holes (6 mm) or areas of perforated zinc (25 mm squares). William R. Bielby, County Beekeeping Officer for North Yorkshire, has suggested that much condensation trouble is removed if the glass is covered by an easily removed layer of insulating material between observations. This has the added benefit of increasing the warmth at the top of the hive and this, coupled with the exclusion of light, encourages the bees to occupy the upper areas of their combs.

If it is wished to go beyond the limited view of the colony revealed by the transparent crownboard, the introduction of windows into the

5

1. Langstroth hive fitted with a glass crownboard.

walls and floorboard opens up both the sides of the flank combs and the ends of all others. The expansion of the brood nest or cluster can then be measured as well as activity on the lower surface of the cluster. The loss of bees in winter can be assessed as well as the uncapping of sealed stores (the discarded cappings falling from the cluster to the hive floor). In summer and autumn propolis screens are built by some races of bees to shield the entrance of the hive and to secure the bottom edges of the frames to the floor. An angled mirror placed below the glass floor will allow the observer to sit on the side away from the entrance.

If it is not wished to cut holes and fit windows into existing hives, Messrs E. H. Thorne, Wragby, Lincs., UK, make up partly glazed

2. A survivor, George Neighbour's improved cottage hive at the Berkshire College of Agriculture in 1971.

3. Simple skep with window. IBRA collection.

4. Transition, British Standard brood box c. 1874 of straw wood and glass, George Neighbour, London. Author's collection.

brood and shallow chambers with simple shutters. They also manufacture perspex crownboards for British Standard and Langstroth pattern hives.

Windows, with shutters, were provided in some of the more elaborate nineteenth- and early twentieth-century skeps and single-walled hives. For double-walled hives the outer walls were in effect shutters wrapping round the entire inner glazed hive. Some nineteenth-century hives were fitted with louvered shutters when the hives were located inside another building.

Shutters are desirable because they exclude light (light inhibits or limits comb construction); they also prevent rain splash from obscuring the glass; they keep the hive warm in bad weather and exclude the sun in good. A glass hive can quickly overheat, particularly when its inhabitants are too few in number effectively to control hive temperature themselves.

Alfred Neighbour (1878) described a number of patterns of windowed custom-built skeps and single- and double-walled hives manufactured by his firm (*see pages* 25–28).

CUSTOM-BUILT MOVABLE-FRAME HIVES

The regular manufacture of observatory hives commenced in the early nineteenth century and was continued into the present century by a number of beekeeping appliance dealers; a typical example was made by E. H. Taylor of Welwyn, Herts, UK, who sold a specially designed single-walled 'observatory' hive, with glass panels let into its side and rear walls, which were covered by small doors. The combs hung parallel to the entrance 'the warm way'. Their number could be reduced by a sliding division board which was also fitted with a glass panel. The hive legs formed an integral part of the structure, as was usual in many nineteenth-century hives, and they were tall enough for the side doors to hang down between them. The raising of the hive on tall legs made it possible for the observer to view the colony when seated on a low stool. Windows were fitted only in the brood chamber of Taylor's hive: additional combs could be added in lightly constructed shallow chambers above the brood box. In this respect, Taylor's differed from Neighbour's hive which had small, fully glazed boxes to contain the honey stores. Other manufacturers made less refined hives by providing shuttered windows in standard brood and shallow chambers.

Not requiring to be weatherproofed, the inner chambers of double-walled hives are more easily adapted to take glass panels. By inserting glass in the place of the wooden panelling normally fitted in the inner cases, a colony can be viewed in its entirety. If large wooden single panels are substituted for the outer casings covering the brood chamber and, say, two supers, the dismantling and reassembling of the hive is simplified. The front section of the case is fixed to the floor and the back and sides can then hinge to it. They can be opened with the minimum disturbance to the colony. Hives of this pattern were produced in England between 1920 and 1939. The interchangeability of the inner boxes between the observation hive and other standard double-walled hives in the apiary was undoubtedly of great advantage.

5. Queen Bee Hive Company, aluminium and glass hive, 1946, outer casing removed.
IBRA collection.

The Queen Bee Hive Company made a metal and glass hive in the late 1940s. These hives, a few of which remain in use today, 1978, were built to take either British Standard brood frames across the hive, or Langstroth frames lengthways: the latter needed to have a small amount cut off their lugs as they were about 6 mm too long overall. The manufacturer's design left quite a large space around the frames so that the bees fill it with brace comb. This demonstrates the need for accurate spacing of combs and the provision of the bee space around them.

In the nineteenth century the addition of one or more glass domes or bells to broad flat-topped skeps and then to movable-frame hives became a common practice as improved methods of manufacture lowered the cost of glass vessels. Victorian and Edwardian beekeepers took great pride in their 'glasses' which were instructive during their preparation as it was possible to see so much of the life of the colony going on within them and, when complete, they would fetch a good price if filled with white virgin honey, free of brood and pollen. The next section describes in some detail the preparation and care of these glass containers.

In use glass supers should always be supported on their own base, kept covered between observations, well ventilated, and if required for exhibition removed as soon as the majority of cells are capped. Any delay in removal may lead to propolization of the glass and staining of the combs.

FIXED-COMB OBSERVATION HIVES TO HOUSE A COMPLETE COLONY

Glass bells The small glass bells described in the preceding section can show the construction of the bees' honey storage combs. A large bell glass also offers opportunities to set up a natural honeybees' nest. Neighbour for his brood nest used large, possibly two-gallon, inverted jars whose upper surface was flat enough to support secondary smaller jars as supers (see figure 2 page 25). He encouraged his honeybees to build regular combs in the large bell by adding a set of horizontal wooden bars near the roof of the jar. The bars were at brood comb spacing about 38 mm centre to centre, with a shallow ridge on their lower side to offer a starting point for the construction of the combs. The wooden grid was supported on a central pedestal, which would later be hidden from view by the bees and combs. Considerable interest was aroused in these hives at shows and exhibitions.

The glass bell Glass bells are still obtainable from laboratory equipment manufacturers and catering equipment suppliers in the UK although their price is high. Less expensive and equally suitable are the glass covers fitted to street lamps. These are also obtainable in hard clear plastic. In either case they should be fitted with a ventilation hole.

Inexpensive glasses can be made by removing the bottom from gallon wine or 'Winchester' quart jars. However, the introduction of hard thin glass in the 1960s has made cutting out of the base a much more difficult task; if possible thick-walled jars should be selected.

6. Inexpensive bell glass made from 1 gallon (4·5 l) wine jar. Author's collection.

Ventilation My own establishment of bee colonies in glass hives confirms Neighbour's opinion that they should be given a free flow of air through them. Neighbour produced a perforated zinc tube which was inserted into the top of several of the different patterns of hive he manufactured. My own attempt at a ventilator will be seen in the picture on page 12. However, as soon as they occupy the whole space available to them bees will propolize up the ventilators' perforations but during the initial establishment phase a through current of air is obtained and condensation is kept to a minimum.

Base support platform Like the 'super' bells, 'brood' bells should stand on a firm base to which the bees can propolize the lower edge of the glass and possibly the tips of their combs. A strong square of blockboard or plywood serves very well, and a central entrance hole should be cut in it to fit over the Porter escape hole in a standard crownboard which may in turn rest either on the top of a hive or on a modified floorboard. I would not suggest cutting a grooved entrance way as the bees will then run over the outer face of the glass and not through the double floor described in the next paragraph.

For a semipermanent or permanent glass observation hive, a double floor should be prepared to control the bees' access to the bell and also provide a feeding arena. A strong top and bottom covering should be added to a standard eke. A 0·9-inch (25-mm) diameter opening is cut into one face of the eke, capable of being covered with a small closure. The upper surface of the platform can either be a standard crownboard or custom built. In the latter case the main opening to the bell should be positioned towards the rear of the platform, say the radius of the bell plus 50 mm, to give room for the outer casing and the insulating jacket. By positioning the bell away from the entrance, a feeding arena can be provided, with a glass panel to permit viewing of the bees' activities within the platform. It may also be felt desirable to provide internal partitions which would direct the bees under the viewing window, and not allow them to build comb or accumulate dross in the inaccessible corners. The viewing window should be covered between observations, otherwise bees may remain in the tunnel, congesting the entrance.

Feeding arena   I am indebted to the late Rupert Lazenby for drawing my attention to a simple feeding arena, to which bees have access
from the entrance passage of the observation hive, or in this case the
base platform tunnel. The feeding arena is placed between the entrance
to the hive and the actual opening into the main nest or brood comb
area. It is thus possible for the bees to defend their nest from robbing
bees who have access to the arena but not to the colony. If the feeder
entrance is located directly into the brood nest, the bees seem uncertain
which is the true entrance to the hive and more easily yield to robbers.

   Another advantage of locating the feeding arena in the entrance is
that the movement to and from the hive of feeding bees can be
observed.

   The arena is formed from a wooden frame a little larger than a standard honey jar. One side of the arena opens into the entrance tunnel
and the upper surface is formed from perforated zinc. On this stands
an inverted jar whose mouth is covered with a double layer of lint held
in place with a rubber band. The jar is filled with strong syrup. Accidental soiling of the arena is avoided if the jar is first inverted over
a dish. When not in use the arena should be covered as bees are
attracted to the light coming in through the gauze and may be unwilling
to return to the hive. They may also fill the arena with rubbish from
the hive including dead bees. The arena should be so constructed that
it can be cleaned out from time to time.

Insulation   The mid-Victorian writers stressed the need to cover
their observation hives with insulating material, for with small colonies
comb construction will cease if the colony becomes chilled. My most
successful observation hives and glass bells have always been covered,
although in hot weather this is reduced or removed. Glass bells should
never be left uncovered in sunlight as they rapidly heat up and the
combs melt. Small sacks of close-woven jute are ideal, but may be difficult to obtain as they are largely superseded by paper or plastic,
although they are still used in the seed trade (care should be taken
that they have not been treated with insecticide). The recently introduced honeycomb padded mailing bags may well prove very suitable as short-term covers. The nineteenth-century classic hives had
custom-made green baize covers or teacosy-like constructions lined

with kapok. Karl von Frisch (1967) describes his cozy in *The Dance Language and Orientation of Bees.*

Comb support   Alfred Neighbour described the preparation of bell glasses in detail, and in addition to the wooded grid described above, provided wooden 'trees' from which the bees could build their combs. Stout suitably-shaped twigs supported on a wooden base permitted a swarm to hang in a natural position and construct comb as in the wild.

Bees can also be induced to build comb directly attached to the glass, so that it is possible to see into some of the cells. It is clear that bees often have difficulty in attaching their comb to highly polished glass surfaces, and this can be overcome by the addition of foundation starters or ribs of wax cast *in situ*. If the upper edge of the strip of foundation is dabbed on to a heated metal block and then rapidly pressed on to the glass it will easily and firmly adhere. Alternatively a low ridge of wax can be cast by melting a little wax in a ladle over a low flame, and then pouring the cooling wax on to the already warmed glass. The glass should be thoroughly warmed; hot wax will shatter cold glass.

Stocking the bell glass   The swarm of honeybees chosen to stock the bell should be selected from known disease-free stock, of even temper, since it is difficult to requeen such a colony unless the bees are driven out by fumigation: an awkward and uncertain task.

The honeybees will most readily occupy the bell if it is given starters of foundation or comb. Some homemade bell jars seem to be unacceptable to bees, due to contamination by what are, to the bees, unpleasant chemicals. When stocking the bell a small swarm or caste should first be collected into a skep so that it can either then be 'run into' the hive in the usual way or it can be shaken directly into the upturned mouth of the glass bell which is then inverted on to its stand, bees and all.

Most bell glass hives are too small to survive as a single unit, and they will need the support of a nucleus either to receive surplus population or to act as a reservoir of worker bees to top up the observation hive. When the observation hive is too crowded it can have its population lowered by artificial swarming of the field bees to the nucleus. This simple technique consists of locating a nucleus alongside the observation hive so that the two foraging forces intermingle. After the two colonies have had time to adjust to each other's presence the observation hive is moved some distance away and the nucleus put in its place. The flying bees from the observation hive will return to their old site and enter and be accepted by the nucleus. If the nucleus in turn becomes overfull, frames of bees and brood can then be removed to other colonies in the apiary. The process can be repeated every time the observation hive becomes overcrowded. On the other hand if the observation hive fails to build up it can have its adult population augmented by reversing the process. The nucleus is moved towards the observation hive, step by step, day by day, and then having stood beside the observation hive for two days it is moved to a new location some distance away. The foraging force will then return to the observation hive, giving it the added field bees it needs. It is advisable during cold or wet weather to feed both lots so that they are in a benign mood during the exchange of field bees and that the donor hive will not suffer unduly the loss of its foragers.

Wintering   The average bell glass hive is possibly too small to overwinter unaided. If the bell and its stand are placed over a mature colony it can be overwintered in the roof space. The host colony is first given a bee-proof gauze screen in place of its crownboard, and the observation hive stood on this with its own entrance to the outside above the screen. It then benefits from the warmth of the host and possibly some food sharing between workers of the two colonies. It is possible to unite the two colonies by using a queen excluder to separate them in a modification of the newspaper method of uniting; the excluder supports the weight of the bell glass which still remains on its own stand. Care must be taken not to cut off a flow of air to the bell glass's occupants by a close-fitting sheet of paper. Air can be admitted to the bell by raising its base on slips of wood thinner than a bee space. If the two clusters fuse—and they may very well not do so—there will be some risk of one of the queens being left on the wrong side of the excluder, or the host bees may well be attracted to the bell and abandon the host colony queen below.

Termination of a stocked bell glass When the bell glass has served its purpose, one is faced with the problem of getting the bees out of the fixed combs within the glass container. It may not be wise to drive them out as one would from a skep; the glass might not stand the drumming. My own technique has been to make up a small queenless colony of about six to eight frames in a standard brood box. After two days and before the new colony has advanced its own queen cells, the bell glass can be united by the newspaper method suggested in the section above. If a queen-right lot acts as host then a two-queen colony may well be created, which will survive as such for some time.

OTHER FIXED-COMB OBSERVATION HIVES

Kolb hive Herman Kolb (1973) devised a simple hive for use in schools and laboratories. It consists of a 10×11 inch (254×280 mm)

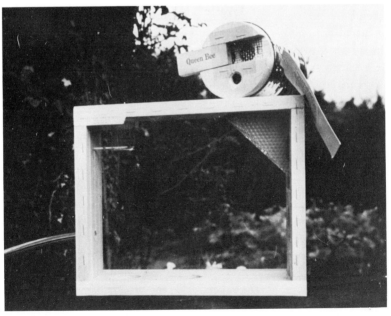

7. Kolb hive with entrance tube to left and bee package above. Author's collection.

frame 4 inches (102 mm) deep with clear plastic sides. A flexible entrance tube is attached through a hole in the side of the box to give the bees free access to the open air. A small feeder is located on the upper surface of the frame and an entrance on one of the sides. A clear plastic tube can be attached to give the bees access through the sash of a window or the walls of a shed. When first supplied two foundation starters are attached to the upper inner surface of the frame. A number of variations of this essentially simple structure permit a range of observations to be made. The hive can be stocked with either package bees supplied in a container capable of attachment to the flexible tube or with a small queenright cast. In the case of the package, the bees are induced to enter the hive by the presence of their caged queen who can be inserted into the hive in the cage in which she has travelled. Details of these hives and supporting literature are obtainable from the maker.

Berkshire hive   In the first half of the nineteenth century a number of hives were invented which were advances on the straw or wicker skep but were not fully developed movable-comb hives. We should consider two of them for they included characteristics of interest if it is wished to construct a honeybee nesting box which will contain a reasonably sized colony. An example of this type—and a number were invented—was developed by J. Sadler of Sonning in Berkshire who devised a hive made of three parts; first, a brood chamber $11\frac{1}{4}$ inches (286 mm) from front to rear, $11\frac{1}{2}$ inches (292 mm) in width and $10\frac{1}{4}$ inches (260 mm) deep inside, having a capacity of about 1300 cubic inches (21,300 cm^3); on three sides were large shuttered windows. The brood chamber was surmounted with two supers half the width of the brood chamber, so that they lay side by side. A fixed board separated them from the brood chamber, the bees having access to the supers through slots in the crownboard $\frac{3}{16}$ inch (5 mm) wide so as to exclude the queen and drones from the supers. The slots could be closed with slides. The super chambers were 10 inches (254 mm) deep and were provided with a cover ribbed on the inside to induce the bees to build six short combs across the supers. Like the brood chamber the supers were provided with windows on two sides. It was estimated each super would hold twenty pounds (9 kg) of honey. These hives were in use

(a)

(b)

8. A fine example of a Nutt collateral hive, possibly by Pettitt of Dover, (a) closed and (b) open. Originally the hive was supported on a floor containing a set of three feeding drawers. IBRA collection.

from 1845 to about 1875, and were intended for use in a house or shed. It is doubtful if this hive was ever used in any large numbers.

Nutt collateral hive   This hive was devised by Thomas Nutt on the collateral principle, where the brood chamber was the middle one of three boxes, those at each side acting as honey storage chambers. A glass bell was also provided over the middle box to act as an additional honey super. The walls of the brood box and adjoining honey chambers were pierced with matching slots so that the bees could pass from one box to the other. The three boxes were placed on a hollow wooden floor which contained feeding drawers and entrance way. The brood box and supers were provided with windows so that the activities of the bees could be observed. This hive was manufactured for about sixty years by various firms in England. The whole concept of depriving the bees of their honey rather than killing the colony over a sulphur pit was developed by Nutt in his book *Humanity to honey bees* (1832). Nutt's hive with its windows, feeder, thermometer and ventilators was an important link between the savants conducting their investigations into the life of the bee

9. Stocked reproduction Nutt hive at Hampshire College of Agriculture c. 1965.

and the creative leaders of the new beekeeping in the later nineteenth century.

Cross-section hive: the Robb Because the classic bell glass was a dome or cylinder, it permitted only one row of cells per comb to be observed edgeways on, the bees either leaving them empty or filling them with nectar or pollen stores. Both Neighbour and Langstroth attempted to overcome the difficulty of observing brood cells by constructing rectangular wood and glass boxes which could be subdivided into smaller units. Their work and that of their contemporaries was restricted until the advent of wired comb foundation made it possible to have readily available quantities of quickly prepared, even sheets of comb. Foundation made it possible to induce bees to build in narrow boxes with the maximum number of comb cells exposed to view.

In 1951, D. Robb described the results of a number of years' work on cross-section hives. In the 1930's and 1940's it became possible to control the input of heat energy to small colonies by the use of electricity; Robb was possibly one of the first to make use of this technology in beekeeping. Since he published his results further important advances have been made in the refinement of equipment. It should not now be so difficult for the beekeeper to set up a controlled environment around a hive and so permit the bees to lay eggs and rear brood at the very edge of their combs, i.e. in cells with one wall of glass.

It still seems useful to record an outline of Robb's hive and some of his findings. He obtained eggs in cells against the glass but they did not hatch unless the weather was very warm, when it was also possible to get foundation drawn out. To get over the screening effect of a large cluster of bees he had to use a very small number of bees. Hive size was also limited by the length of the standard electric light bulbs he used as a source of heat. The apparatus consisted of a ventilated outer case double glazed on both sides, and an inner 'hive'. The heaters were in the floor of the outer case. The efficiency of the heaters was increased and the light glare cut out by painting the light bulbs with heat-resistant paint. Robb found it did not prove necessary to use a thermostat to control the temperature, but it was essential to fit strawboard covers when the hive was not under observation.

If more efficient insulating material than strawboard was used as shutters—and far better insulation is available today—heat escape vents were required. The length of the hive was limited by the length of the light bulbs and their associated fittings and the height of the case by the 'effect of the heating arranged' [about $9\frac{1}{2}$ inches (610 mm)].

The 'hive' fitted into the heating case consisted of three units supported on a rectangular frame; the middle one carried a single comb to face the observer, the other two cross-sections of combs. The centre unit was so devised that only one half of a comb was used by the bees, the other being cut away so that the cell bases were tight against the glass wall. A bee space was allowed over the cell openings on the other face.

The Robb hive was essentially purpose built and I have no evidence that any attempt was made to build more than those needed for educational work by Robb and his friends. His own published details would allow others to be built as required.

This summary of the stocking technique and the effects of feeding are worth noting. The Robb hive was stocked with 500 grams of bees with their queen. These were taken from a normal colony and shaken into a specially prepared crate. Its lid was provided with a hollow pivot similar to the one in the base of the tunnel leading to the hive. By placing the complete hive over the hollow pivot of the crate lid and withdrawing a closing slide the bees had direct access to the hive.

A cloth previously soaked in a solution of carbolic acid was laid against the perforated zinc sides under the cluster of bees to encourage them to vacate the crate and establish themselves in the hive.

Robb fed his bees regularly with syrup from a bottle at the top of the hive. He found that within 12 hours the queen bee commenced laying against the glass in the middle unit, and within a week the worker bees had made good progress in comb building in the other two units. When nectar was coming in no further feeding was given and daily progress was observed and recorded. When the unit became overloaded with honey, or otherwise not so interesting, a spare unit was substituted.

CHAPTER TWO

HIVES TO HOLD A SINGLE RANGE OF COMB

So far we have considered the housing of colonies where their nest is in the natural form for European honeybees, i.e. the combs are built side by side, the flank combs sheltering the central ones used for brood rearing. In the multicomb hive much of the detailed life of the colony is obscured by these flank combs. Where a more detailed examination is needed then the honeybees must be given a nesting box in which they can have only a single range of comb which is therefore fully exposed to view, as in the unicomb hive. Except for short-term usage—at most one or two days—at shows, fairs and lectures, in the unicomb hive life support factors become critically important and we need to consider them in planning and constructing the hive. We must provide just sufficient space to allow only one comb to be constructed and at the same time be able to feed the colony and to provide for flight, foraging and ventilation. I have therefore confined myself in this section to permanent and semi-permanent unicomb hives and placed temporary unicomb hives in a separate section.

DEVELOPMENT IN THE NINETEENTH CENTURY

In describing framed unicomb and leaf hives Edward Bevan (1838) gave a brief history of the observation hive and the allied development

23

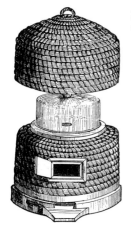

Fig. 1. Neighbour's 'An improved cottager's hive' with window and single bell glass.

Fig. 2. Neighbour's 'improved cottager's hive' with 3 middle-sized bell glasses and ventilators.

10. *left*. Transition from tiered skep to wooden hive. 'The Stewarton', note small shuttered windows on each tier.

Fig. 3. Neighbour's 'Ladies' Observation Hive' with large and small bell glasses, support for the combs and outer ventilator cover.

Fig. 4. Neighbour's 'Philadelphia Frame Hive.'

(a)

(b)

Fig. 5. Neighbour's 'Unicomb Observation Hive' (a) fixed for use outdoors and (b) on turntable for use indoors. Note plug to feeder removed.

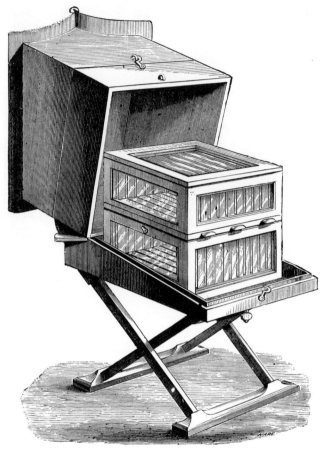

Fig. 6. Neighbour's glass walled hive viewed from the rear with the outer cover raised.

of the Huber leaf hive, three paragraphs of which are worth quoting in full.

Narrow hives for experimental purposes, with large glazed doors on each side, have been used by amateur apiarians for many years. That of *Reaumur* was too wide: it allowed the construction of two combs parallel to each other. This form is unfavourable, as it secludes all observation of the proceeding of the bees in the interspace between the combs. *Bonnet* recommended a hive, the doors of which should be only so far asunder as to allow the building of one comb between them. This suggestion was successfully adopted by *Huber*; and to prevent the bees from building short transverse combs, instead of a single one, parallel to the sides of the hive, he laid the foundation himself, by fastening a piece of empty comb to the ceiling of the box.

The hive in which *Huber* conducted his first experiments, had only an interspace of an inch and a half (38 mm) between the glass doors, so that the bees could not cluster on the surfaces of the comb, and yet had room to pass freely over it. *John Hunter* recommended the diameter of these narrow hives to be 3 inches (76 mm) and the superficies of the sides of sufficient size to afford stowage for a summer's work. *Dunbar* with his mirror-hive, constructed somewhat like *Huber's*, had been able to make some interesting observations on the economy of the bee. The distance of his glass doors from each other is 1⅔ inch (45 mm); the height of the hive about 18 inches (457 mm), the width about two feet (610 mm). Across the centre of the mirror-hive, he introduced a light frame, which although apparently dividing the hive into four compartments, allowed the bees a free passage; the light was excluded by a pair of folding shutters each side.

Huber carried the principle of these experimental hives still further; he joined several of them together with hinges, which were so contrived as to admit of easier removal; as the frames or leaves, as *Huber* called them, were not glazed, they afforded a free communication with each other.

Today we would not regard the Huber hive as an observation hive, because the colony is extensively disturbed when the leaves are parted,

(a)

(b)

11. Huber's leaf hive:
(a) upper: closed
(b) lower: opened   IBRA collection.

12. Single frame decorated nineteenth-century observation hive. IBRA collection.

but we should not forget that it was an important step in the development of both observation and orthodox frame hives.

Bevan completed his chapter on unicomb and leaf hives with notes on a hive that he constructed. Essentially the Bevan unicomb hive was made up of three parts:

(1) A revolving floorboard with two central entrance ways supported on a post set in the ground. The bees were allowed to fly from the entrance furthest from the observer. The hive 'proper', roof and doors were attached to the floorboard by metal rods.

(2) A rectangular frame 2 inches (50 mm) by 1 inch (25 mm) thick, two feet (610 mm) long by 18 inches (457 mm) high, divided into four by light cross-members $\frac{3}{8}$ inch (9 mm) square, the latter supporting the natural comb which the bees were induced to build parallel with the glass by starter combs. The glass walls were mounted on frames attached to the body of the hive by hooks and eyes. Bevan stressed the need to have the walls exactly $1\frac{4}{5}$ inch (45 mm) apart.

(3) $1\frac{1}{2}$ inches (38 mm) thick shutters and glazed sides enclosed the hive to protect the bees from extremes of temperature, together with a detachable roof.

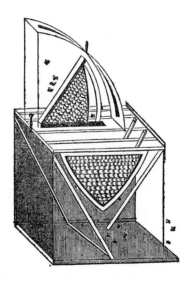

Fig. 7. Major Munn's Bar Frame Hive. From Pettitt *The Management of Bees*.

Langstroth (1857) in his *A practical treatise on the hive and the honey-bee* described briefly the use and benefits of 'observing hive and parlour-observing hives': particularly for people living in cities.

Neighbour, writing twenty years later, gave a detailed description of 'unicomb' observation hives for use indoors and out. Indeed he defined the essential requirements of the modern movable-comb observation hive with its unimpeded view of the combs through double glazing, combs interchangeable with the hives in the apiary, indirect lighting, glass-walled entrance tube, feeder, ventilation and insulation. Neighbour suggested the use of one-, two- and six-comb hives, where the combs formed a single viewable range.

FURTHER DEVELOPMENTS: THE TWENTIETH CENTURY

Herrod-Hempsall   Herrod-Hempsall (1937) outlined the development of the observation hive and gave small, extremely detailed drawings of a rotating hive as well as illustrations of three- and six-comb hives. The Herrod-Hempsall hive became the standard observation hive of British beekeeping, all British beekeeping equipment manufacturers offering observation hives which were essentially simplified versions of the Neighbour/Herrod-Hempsall pattern, holding a combination of brood and extracting combs, with possibly an additional row of sections. One brood and two shallow, or two brood and one shallow comb being common combinations. The more expensive hives are made to rotate around a central axis.

The essential weakness of these hives was the standardization on the long-lug British frame which made the upright members of the hive more complex than they need be if short-lug frames were used: it is also true that in a search for economy, the hives have been built to a lower specification than is desirable. In practice, they offer only a ready-made core to which need be added weather-proof cover, glazed entrance tube, feeding arena and insulated cover.

Karl von Frisch   As was suggested in the introduction, observation hives, although rating considerable interest and forming part of numerous short articles for the bee press and extension literature in the USA have received no major published examination in English. A popular untranslated monograph was published in Russian (Khalifman, 1960). Von Frisch's *Dance language and orientation of bees* is the only book known to me which gives a sound detailed examination of the preparation and use of the observation hive. Indeed the whole work is a demonstration of the application of this type of hive to the elucidation of bee behavioural problems and is a model for a book of this kind.

Von Frisch in his second chapter sets out his work on the construction and use of observation hives under the following subheadings:

(1) The observation hive
(2) Heatable observation hives
(3) Rooms for bees
(4) Marking bees with numbers
(5) We set up an artificial feeding place (*sic*)
(6) Automatic recording of visits to observation place
(7) Cleaning the equipment; scents as a source of error
(8) How bees are put to work or brought home
(9) Measurement of the tempo and direction of dancing
(10) Selection of the bees

Von Frisch was satisfied that the work of Gontarski (1943) demonstrated that almost five hundred bees developed a normal social organization and that Gesthke found five hundred to one thousand bee colonies had the same division of labour as normal colonies. Von Frisch recognized the need to maintain a proper temperature and so provided wooden covers lined with padded material. In cool weather, especially at night, a thickly padded outer cover proved useful, this being drawn over the hive like a tea cosy. Double glazing served to prevent further cooling, the outer pane being hinged to the framework of the hive so as to open during warm weather. Because von Frisch wished to observe the entrance and egress of his bees, he provided a movable wedge in the entrance. This diverted towards the observer the bees passing along the glass-roofed entrance tunnel.

Like Bevan, von Frisch regarded the space between the glass and the comb as critical if unimpeded observation is to be made, and he suggested 4·6–4·8 mm, thus preventing the construction of brace comb. The overall size of the structure to hold the framed combs being dependent on the frame size in use in the colony from which the observation hive is stocked. In portable hives, small wedges can be applied to the frames to secure them.

The von Frisch hive was built out of six basic parts in addition to its combs:

(1) outer padded cozy
(2) inner protective wooden covers
(3 & 4) two double glass windows
(5) main structure, recessed to take the frame lugs and supported on the bench or observation platform by
(6) two feet screwed to the bottom and normally set at right angles to the hive, but during movement folding beneath.

Two holes were provided on the narrow face of the main structure, one low down for an entrance which when in use was joined to the glazed entrance tunnel, and when out of use was covered with a gauze screen. The other hole pierced the top surface and served both as a ventilator during moves, or to give access to a shallow trough for feeding. The carrying handle was screwed to the upper edge.

The von Frisch semi-portable bee house   When a colony is exposed to direct sunlight the dance pattern of the bees is distorted if they can see the blue sky. To obtain observations with the minimum of disturbance von Frisch placed his observation hives in small portable huts. In one pattern the hive was housed in a hut of its own and the observer in another. The huts were placed side by side and the intervening walls removed. Each hut was about the size of those used by night-watchmen, their small size being dictated by the need for easy portability.

A larger and more elaborate hut was made in three horizontal sections. The hive's base board was extended and protected by a shallow wall of hardboard, the observer could either sit at the side or move round to the rear of the hive. On to this base clipped the middle section with shuttered walls and a door. Then on to this upper structure was secured the third or roof section made of a simple curve of hardboard with wide overhanging eaves.

In both huts enough light to work by entered under the eaves or from below the base board, if not the wall shutters could be taken down.

A diffuse illumination was provided by drawing curtains across the spaces left by removal of one or more of the shutters. During observation light-coloured clothing was found to be distracting and a black apron reaching to the neck was worn. Reflection was thus reduced, a clear view obtained and any distortion of the bees' behaviour avoided.

The tiltable observation hive   Von Frisch also devised a tiltable observation hive which permitted the comb to be held at any angle between vertical and horizontal. The hive was supported on two brass tubes fastened to the front and rear ends of the main structure, and retained in wooden blocks attached to the base board. A callibrated scale registered the angle of declination. The entrance to the hive was through one of the brass tubes.

The heated observation hive to take a single range of comb   In seeking to extend the season for his observations von Frisch used both a bee flight room and a heatable observation hive. The provision of a flight room is a useful experimental technique but falls outside the more general use of the observation hive, and is therefore not considered here.

The need for heated and insulated observation hives may not be as great today as in the past, with more efficient laboratory and school central heating systems. However, during holidays and at weekends, institution heating may well be reduced to a level inimical to small honeybee colonies.

Von Frisch placed a portable observation hive in a larger box with glass panels devised by M. Lindauer. In this case heating was from an infra-red bulb controlled by a thermostat.

More precise temperature regulation was obtained in a hive devised by H. D. Braüninger. Comb with one side cut back to the midrib was placed in a narrow hive in which heating elements on the side farthest from the observer and in the place of the removed cells. Bees were induced to dance on the single remaining comb surface.

In addition to electrically controlled heating, a cooling supply of air could be given in warm weather.

Herrod-Hempsall (1937) gave plans of an electrical hive devised by A. Parkinson in which electric heating elements were contained in the detachable shutters enclosing the glass sides of the hive. Provision was also made for elaborate feeding arrangements and provided for microscopical examination of the comb.

Numerous workers have attempted to heat hives by the warm wall method, which although suitable for single static hives has very real limitations. The hive cannot be taken to the apiary without risk of damage to the wiring. And in addition to the bees being excited by the opening of the shutters, prolonged observation may possibly lead to chilling of the brood.

Norman Element working at Rothamsted Experimental Station has overcome the limitations of the warm wall system by separating the heat source from the hive. Simple interchangeable two-frame observation hives slot into deep plinths in which are fitted three thermostatically-controlled one-third-kilowatt electric fire elements. The hive of bees therefore stands in a column of warm, temperature-controlled air, which rises by natural convection around the hive body. As the experimental work progresses the hive can be removed from its base and relocated or interchanged with other similar hives. The more delicate heating unit can remain firmly attached to its supporting bench or table. For restocking the hive can easily be conveyed to the apiary so that frames of bees can be exchanged or experimental work undertaken.

Clear perspex is used in place of glass, thus simplifying the hives' construction and making it possible to remove either comb without disturbing the other. There is no supporting frame between the combs, two perspex sheets forming one side and butting together horizontally across the hive. In at least one hive small removable discs were cut in the perspex so that almost any part of the comb surface is accessible without major disturbance to the colony. When in use at Rothamsted the observation hives are shaded from direct sunlight but not kept covered.

Dr C. G. Butler, former head of the Entomology Section at Rothamsted, in a private communication, has stressed the need to provide

(a)

13. Von Frisch's portable observation hive
(a) *above:* open showing glazed sashes;
(b) *right:* closed showing padded outer cover.

(b)

both food and water under laboratory conditions and, if the brood is to occupy the maximum area, entrance tube draught should be prevented by inserting a grille of gauze in its underside to break the flow of air. Without the grille a section of the comb near the entrance will be uninhabited by the bees.

The Farrar multiunit observation hive   The late Dr C. L. Farrar, professor and head of the Bee Culture Investigations of University of Wisconsin and the United States Department of Agriculture, designed a large unicomb hive whose component parts could be manipulated indoors without loss of bees.

The hive was built up out of six separate single-frame units supported within a larger main frame. The main frame of wood and slotted angle was provided with a metal cleanout tray and an entrance tube, and was supported by one single metal tubular leg. Each subunit was built up from wooden ends and side bars supporting clear 'Plexiglas' sheets. The shallow frames slotted into these holders. The rear section of the main frame was detachable so that any individual unit could be removed by inserting metal slides or the whole could be taken down section by section. Metal screens were used in place of the slides if the bees were to be confined to the subunits for long.

During assembly or dismounting each of the units could be secured with masking tape. The possibility of inserting comb cut into sections and placed at right angles to the observer was discussed in Farrar's description of his hive, this technique making it possible to view the use of cells in depth. One of the frame holders could also be modified to take a feeder.

The data sheet (A2491) provided by the Cooperative Extension Programme of the University of Wisconsin gave details of construction, installation from an existing colony or package bees, and its maintenance during the summer and autumn. Possible simple experiments were suggested.

14. Observation hive at Rothamsted Experimental Station, with heating wires visible in back wall; insulated cover to left of picture.

15A Norman Element's hive with access ports cut into perspex walls at Rothamsted Experimental Station.

15B 'Hive' body to take long lug British Standard frames, perspex walls removed.

15c Heating unit with hive body dismounted.

CHAPTER THREE

THE CONSTRUCTION OF AN OBSERVATION HIVE FOR GENERAL USE

So far we have traced the development of multicomb and unicomb hives during the last 150 years. In this section I wish to look in greater detail at the basic elements in design of new or the adaptation of existing unicomb hives for general use. Commercially manufactured observation hives may be made more useful by careful adaptation and although initially expensive may offer the person who is not a wood worker an opportunity, which would not otherwise exist, of owning an observation hive.

I have drawn attention on page 34 to the fact that no specialized study of the observation hive has been published in English, nor, so far as I know, are plans readily available except for one or two individualistic designs. Possibly this is due to the ready availability of manufactured hives but it may be due to the potentially limited market for precise scale plans for any one type of hive. Each designer is soon aware of the problems facing him when considering the many frame sizes which exist. There are for example in Britain two commonly used frame sizes with both brood and extracting depths with the further option of either long or short lugs as well as hives to take Langstroth and Dadant frames. In Europe there is greater diversity in width and depth measurements as well as totally lugless frames. Even in countries

45

where both the Langstroth and Dadant hive predominate a choice of comb size exists within these two models.

In this chapter, therefore, I wish to discuss the fundamental measurements needed in every unicomb hive irrespective of the frame size, as well as the other requirements which determine the degree of weather-proofing required or if provision for a rotating stand is needed.

My own reaction to the problem of a lack of plans has been either to draw one for myself using the frame I use in the apiary (Langstroth deep), to copy an existing hive or to modify a purchased hive, adding the refinements I require for the work in hand.

FUNDAMENTAL MEASUREMENTS

In planning a unicomb observation hive two essential measurements are needed:

(1) the between-glass measurement
(2) the frame size with associated bee space

Very few writers have touched on the between-glass internal measurement—essential if the hive is to have movable combs. Edward Bevan gave a wide measurement of $1\frac{2}{3}$ inch (42 mm); Alfred Neighbour was content to say 'the width of the hive between the glasses of the sashes (windows of the hive) is just sufficient to admit of one thickness of comb, with space on each side for the bees to pass and repass between the glass and the comb'. In other words the between-glass measurement is equal to the space between the midribs of any two adjacent brood combs. Grahame Walton, in preparing detailed specifications for the metrication of the New Zealand Langstroth hive, discusses a number of important measurements needed in general hive construction which are applicable to the unicomb observation hive. He pointed out that the 'ideal' spacing of brood frames, midrib to midrib, is $1\frac{3}{8}$ inch (32–34 mm).

In general Hoffman pattern frames are spaced at $1\frac{3}{8}$ inch (32–34 mm) centres, and the British standard frames are arranged at $1\frac{1}{2}$ inch (36–38 mm) centres when metal spacers are used in the brood nest and honey supers.

Failure to recognize the importance of the between-glass measurement can either make it impossible to insert standard combs from another hive or the bees will extend their combs out towards the glass (alternatively they may build secondary combs between the main surface of the comb and the glass). Some observation hives are deliberately constructed to give this extra space on one side only to demonstrate:

(a) the importance of the bee space
(b) the construction of extended cells for honey storage
(c) the use of brace comb to steady the main comb to the glass
(d) the use by the bees of burr comb which uses the glass as a cell base

In both (c) and (d) the observer can see into some of the cells and note the storage of nectar and pollen.

It is unlikely that brood would be reared against the glass even if eggs were laid in them; it would be exceptional for the eggs to hatch into viable larvae in such an exposed position.

Frame size and bee space   All unicomb hives contain one or more framed combs supported by the outer structure of the hive body, the combs being covered on either side with detachable framed window sashes. The combs, in their frames, are located so as to allow a bee space around the edge of the frames except where they are supported on the lower side of their lugs by the hive body.

For all practical purposes a bee space can be taken as $\frac{1}{4}$ inch (6 mm) and derives from the bees' practice of sealing any opening less than $\frac{3}{16}$ inch (5 mm) with propolis or spaces larger than $\frac{5}{16}$ inch (8 mm) with comb. Hive parts separated by a bee space tend to be left free of infilling, thus allowing the bees to pass through the space and the beekeeper to remove the parts at will.

A bee space should also be allowed above the lugs and $\frac{1}{16}$ inch (1·5 mm) at their ends (the slight side-to-side movement of the frames being called top-bar play); in long-lug frames the end of the lug may extend through the hive body and no additional space is then allowed above the lug. Some propolization may build up where the lug passes through the wall but it is normally insufficient to prevent the easy removal of the frame.

In Britain the use of the Smith short-lug version of the British Standard frame simplifies construction. Long-lug frames can be cut down to ¾ inch (18 mm) as in the Smith hive or ⅝ inch (16 mm) as in the Lang-stroth hive. In an apiary in which long-lug frames are used a few short-lug frames can be kept in one colony for use in observation hives.

If more than one frame is required in the observation hive then a bee space should be allowed between the frames. It is an advantage to give slightly more room at the bottom of the hive to allow for the

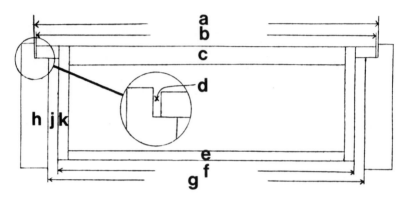

a. inner rebate length	f. bottom-bar length
b. top-bar length	g. inner length of hive body
c. top bar	h. hive body
d. top-bar play	j. side bee-space
e. bottom bar	k. end bar

Suspension of frame within hive body

To maintain a full interchange of equipment there are only three possible measurements for the inner rebated length, 18·9, 19, 19·13 inches (482 mm, 485 mm, 486 mm). The inner rebated length cannot be greater than 19·13 inches (486 mm) otherwise standard 18·9 inches (482 mm) top bars would fit too loosely, nor less than 484 mm, for then the 19 inch (485 mm) top bar would not fit satisfactorily. A metric top bar cannot be any longer than 19 inches (485 mm) otherwise it would not fit within an existing hive body, nor any shorter than 18·8 inches (480 mm) otherwise excessive top-bar play would result.

Metric specification
    top-bar length: 18·9 inches (482 mm)
    inner rebated length: 19 inches (485 mm)
    top-bar play: 0·059 inch (1·50 mm)
From G. M. Walton, *Proposals for the Metric Langstroth Hive*, (MAF New Zealand) page 8.

accumulation of debris. In a bottom-entrance hive a deep, say $\frac{1}{2}$ inch, (13 mm) approach to the entrance tube is desirable to prevent blockage and give the colony additional air space in the hive body.

Under certain conditions when sealed stores are being rapidly consumed the bees produce appreciable amounts of moisture which may well collect along the bottom edge of the comb or at the entrance. In very small colonies there can be, if the bees are unwilling to break cluster, sufficient dead bees' bodies accumulated to block the entrance tube, thus effectively sealing the colony in. In the Farrar hive a removable trash tray is provided to receive the debris from the hive.

DRAWING A PLAN

I am indebted to Graham Walton for the diagram of a hive cross-section given on page 48. Measurements of the frames in use in the apiary may be inserted on to it to give the basic vertical and horizontal measurements of the hive under construction. The length over the lugs should be such that frames are neither too tight nor too loose, with top bar play about 1.5 mm at each end. If it is wished to support the frame lug on a metal rabbet then the end rebate depth should be increased accordingly. A bee space above the frame and between frames should be included in the measurements.

Number of frames In planning the unicomb hive it should be borne in mind that this hive at its best is a cross-section through a standard colony; it must therefore reflect the bees' use of the lower and upper brood nest with its pattern of cleaned cells, eggs developing into larvae, larvae to pupae, open pollen and nectar storage, with finally sealed food reserves. It should, if possible, show the pollen arch between the brood nest and the nectar and honey stores.

It is an advantage to design the hive to hold more than one comb since this permits the replacement of combs during the course of the season or permits the giving of added stores or sheets of foundation when preparing demonstrations. Two brood and one shallow frame or three brood frames, gives greater flexibility than the two brood frame hives often sold commercially.

Hives to take a large number of frames have been constructed either

16. The author's own outdoor observation hive with shutters closed.

in the vertical or horizontal dimension. Although such hives will require skill in their care, their physical limits are more than likely to be set by the size and shape of the accommodation to house them. At the Rothamsted Experimental Station, an eighteen frame British Standard brood hive was constructed and operated, its available 'cell-age' being about 90,000. This hive held a full mature colony with a normal population number. It was three frames high and six deep, heated by a wired-wall method using heating wires embedded in the outer glass windows of its double glazing. A large amount of my own

17. Crundwell's observation hive, Stoneleigh, Warwickshire.

work has been conducted with hives of two deep and one shallow British Standard frames—about 12,000 cells. A hive with this number can have any one comb replaced without destroying the colony. Such a hive can be stocked from a four-frame nucleus.

Location: indoors or out   Most observation hives are located within a building, with or without added heat, for only indoors can a small colony be expected to stand much chance of overwintering. However even in the United Kingdom observation hives can be kept outside throughout much of the summer. I have for about twenty years stocked the two-brood-frame hive shown on page 50. This small hive is sheltered from rain by the overhanging eves of its canopy and by shutters which also protect the glass. Additionally, in hot weather, a canvas shelter keeps off the direct sun; at night a hessian cozy is added.

In normal use outside, the hive is stabilized by four brick blocks, one on each leg, which can be screwed to the benching when staged at an exhibition.

Two other examples of a sheltered support are the von Frisch hives housed in portable huts, described in detail on page 35, and those prepared by Jim Crundwell at the British Beekeepers' Association Bee Garden on the show ground of the Royal Agricultural Society of England, Stoneleigh, Warwickshire, which are supported in a steel frame with additional weather-proofing. In the picture, page 51, the entrance tube is carried above the heads of the observers, and is positioned so that its upper end is protected by a cowl to prevent rain entering the tube.

To rotate or not   In England there is a long tradition, extending back to the early nineteenth century, that the observation hive should be so devised that it can rotate on a central spindle. The observer is thus enabled to sit still, and the hive turns before him. In addition to increasing the initial complexity of the hive and therefore its cost, there is the added disadvantage of a major disturbance to the bees each time the hive is moved. In schools and other public places this can be several times an hour, so that any experimental work is invalidated.

In many locations the bees will soon establish which side of the comb is most suited to their main breeding area and it may be some time before the queen will move to the disadvantaged side. Regular rotation will make it difficult to determine if the bees have a preferred side and indeed may hinder the establishment and growth of the colony.

In a rotating hive, the bees obtain entry to the hive through the supporting spindle usually at the mid point of the base, or at the end nearest the wall, in which case the hive can turn only through 90°. It is usual to provide the entrance through the lower spindle; I have no record of an upper-entrance rotating hive being constructed although there is no technical reason why the entrance should not be above the colony cluster.

In many rotating hives the weight and stress produced by the rotary action is shared equally at the upper and lower points of attachment. In the hives devised by Alfred Neighbour, James Lee* and William Herrod-Hempsall, the whole hive was supported on a metal turntable, without any upper support being provided.

Except as a demonstration of technical enterprise there is little advantage in a rotating hive unless it is to be used in the most confined space, for example where it is wished to have a hive built into a cupboard where it would be left undisturbed for most of the time.

The hive body, windows and cover   In the unicomb observation hive, the hive body is the width of at least one frame and the depth of as many as are required to form the hive. Its construction will largely be dictated by the requirements of the observer provided the essential measurements already outlined are adhered to.

Body   In its construction, it must be strong enough to give rigidity to the combs and the glass windows; it should allow for the entrance holes, feeder and additional ventilation. It may require supporting feet or to slot into some sort of framework. Refinement in design should not obscure its essential purpose of holding the window sashes and retaining the bees. It must not warp in use or be incapable of receiving additional fittings as work with the hive develops.

Windows   The windows of many observation hives are double glazed to give better insulation: the glass should be fixed in a firm frame which is strong enough to withstand some leverage if the window is opened after propolization. I have had to put a hive into a very warm room to soften up the propolis before the windows could be opened. Von

---

* Such a hive is illustrated on the dust wrapper of this book.

18. Thorne's Rotary Observation Hive. Note feeding arena to right of hive body.
IBRA collection.

19. D. Robb's unheated perspex and wood model. IBRA collection.

Frisch provided a double window, the outer one being removable during observation or in hot weather.

Shutters   Under certain conditions it is possible to leave the hive uncovered all the time—bees become accustomed to continuous light. If, however, for protection against cold or accidental damage the glass is covered with wooden shutters, when they are removed the bees will run excitedly over the glass and all the observer will see is the underside of a large number of worker bees. In an outdoor position or an unheated room, baize-lined shutters or polyurethane panels will provide a large measure of protection and insulation.

Cozy   Under cool summer conditions the unheated hive will benefit from a large over-all warm padded cover or cozy. This can envelop the feeder, if it is attached to the hive, and hang down below the bottom of the main body. It should not be tight enough to impede ventilation and can be held clear of the hive by a wire frame. A hessian or burlap sack is a good substitute for a custom-made covering; it has the advantage of being of fairly open texture and is unlikely to suffocate the bees.

Position of the entrance   My own experience of observation hives has been limited to lower entrance observation hives but William Bielby has drawn my attention to the advantages he found in placing the entrance at the top, clear of the floor of the hive, so that under adverse weather conditions, if there is any accumulation of dead bees on the floor of the hive, the living bees are not prevented from leaving the hive.

Entrance tube   Most factory-made observation hives have entrance tubes opening out from the bottom of the hive body. With rotary models this is generally essential since the supporting spindle shaft provides the opening from the hive to the horizontal entrance. Fixed hives allow for the entrance to be located on any side to suit the observer, the situation of the hive, or the work to be done.

Long entrance tubes have disadvantages. The bees may experience difficulty in locating the outside opening to the tube; small colonies may find the effort of extracting the hive debris too great and the tube may become blocked. Care should also be taken to see that the tube does not funnel in wind and rain; the introduction of a gauze section in the wall of the tube may reduce the effect of strong draughts.

My own experience with glazed tubes is that although they enable the observer to follow the activities of the bees and to check if the tube is functioning properly, bees will be strongly attracted to the light entering the windows in the tube and will remain on the transparent areas seeking to get out. They will be loath either to enter the hive or to pass out of the open end of the tube if this is darkened by the outside wall of the building housing the hive. Large numbers of bees will remain in the tube, effectively blocking the passage of those bees who have established the route to the outside. This problem can be overcome by fitting shutters over the tube windows: the effect of light on tube use can then be demonstrated.

It is also an advantage to be able to close the hive where it is joined to the tube so that both the tube and the feeding area can be cleaned out without the bees escaping into the room. If the hive is shut off it can be removed leaving the tube and other fittings *in situ*. Robber bees too can be excluded; observation hives require regular feeding and are therefore attractive to bees from other nearby colonies. It may be advisable to seal off the hive if robbing develops.

Feeder Unless there is some overriding experimental reason for introducing the feeder directly into the main hive, an arena feeder as described on page 14 can be included with the entrance tube fittings. This too should be provided with an observation window and facilities for opening and cleaning.

Alighting board One of the major disadvantages of modern single-wall hives is the situation of their entrances, so near the ground that the beekeepers cannot easily observe the events at the entrance in detail. Modern beekeepers are thus deprived of much that interested earlier generations of beekeepers or those who still have their colonies raised some distance from the ground. I have observed bees living in a log with an entrance about 3 feet (1 m) from the ground. The behaviour of the colony during swarming can be recorded with much greater ease than when a standard hive is used with its entrance at or a little above ground level. A diary of observations at the entrance to the hive would add a further dimension to a school observation hive.

In constructing the entrance tube to the hive provision of a small sloping flightboard is desirable. A screened entrance makes it both easier to observe the bees and for them to locate their entrance. If the building housing the hive offers large areas of uniform surface, to have the funnel entrance clearly marked with blue paint will help the bees and also warn passers-by to watch out for the bees.

Some loss of foragers will be noticed if the alighting board is smooth and remains wet for some time after rain. A small area of perforated zinc or metal rust-proofed gauze will provide the rough surface the bees require.

CHAPTER FOUR

LOCATING AN OBSERVATION HIVE

The unicomb hive, as has been made clear in chapter three, places the bees at some disadvantage if they are to maintain proper ventilation, temperature and humidity. Locational factors must therefore play an important part in the choice of a site, the wrong site making it difficult to maintain a hive for very long. Exposure to full sun can lead to severe distress and even damage to the brood and comb.

In selecting a hive site three essential groups of requirements should be considered those of

(1) the bees,
(2) the beekeepers
(3) the experimental work to be undertaken.

In certain circumstances the third group may well be of paramount importance and all other elements sacrificed to it, but in this chapter we are more concerned with the preservation of the bees as a colony unit.

The bees' most essential requirement is a dry sheltered home, protected from external enemies and weather, and located in an area with ample pollen and nectar. Any shortfall in these can easily be made up by nectar feeding and the use of pollen substitutes. In a dry heated building it may be desirable to feed water as well as syrup.

The indoor observation hive may well be subject to draughts which will affect the brood position in the hive, especially in unicomb hives.

20. J. L. Sargent's outdoor hive at Kent Farm Institute (now Hadlow College), Sittingbourne 1956.

21. G. Hawthorne's observation skep at Berkshire College of Agriculture 1977.

Those kept covered with a cozy will be less subject to this sort of damage but it may be a small but limiting factor in certain circumstances.

In addition to the factors affecting the bees ability to maintain the economy of their hive, it should always be borne in mind that even small colonies contain several hundred workers whose flightpath to the hive entrance will need to be kept clear if stings are to be avoided. When children are to make regular observations the hive should be placed in a sheltered position so that bees will not be blown on to the young observers. A hive placed near a regularly used path will also cause trouble, for bees fly during most weeks of the year—on mild days in winter large numbers leave the hive, circling round, even if they do not venture far away.

So long as colonies remain undisturbed it is possible to locate them on small garden plots, provided the mowing and other cultivation takes place when the bees are inactive. However, manipulation will make the bees extremely alert and they will then attack anyone entering the plot.

In the main, multicomb hives require a less critical location than unicomb hives, but they do require a far larger flight area in front of and around the hive itself.

Geoffrey Hopkinson, in a private communication, has described the bee houses he has used in educational projects in Staffordshire. The observation hives are located inside small sheds on the less frequented parts of school grounds; the children being able to observe the bees inside the shed without risk or the necessity for veils or bee-proof clothing.

Foraging honeybees soon learn the precise location of their hive, returning to it even if the hive, their queen and brood combs are moved some distance away. Hives must be relocated to distances in excess of 1 mile (1.6 km) if the return of a large proportion of the foraging force is to be avoided. It is therefore essential that every care should be taken in the positioning of an observation hive, for once it is installed it can not be moved easily to another site in the same area.

CHAPTER FIVE

STOCKING AND CARE OF THE OBSERVATION HIVE

Basic planning So far we have examined the basic requirements of bees and comb, and from this it can be seen that stocking the observation hive is not just a matter of taking a comb or two from any colony in the apiary, but rather, if the work is to be of any real value, a considered step-by-step process leading to a carefully defined goal. This planning stage is necessary if we are to get the best out of the resources of comb and bees available to us and if we are not to waste time and money.

We need first to be clear whether we are providing a temporary, semipermanent or permanent observation hive. The temporary hive which is being set up for a one or two day exhibition provides the least problems as its inmates will have very little opportunity to adjust to their new surroundings, whereas the permanent and semipermanent hive will effectively become a self-contained unit needing sufficient reserves of pollen and honey to last for some days until it can obtain a regular supply of its own. The age distribution of the original inmates must be such as to provide a good foraging force of several hundred bees.

In addition to the usual display function of the observation hive it may be required for serious work of an experimental or observational nature. Although in these circumstances the professional scientist will

63

already have the expertise to make the basic planning decisions, the beekeeper entering into a project either on his own or in collaboration with a student, should spend some time listing his reasons for using the hive, and the points he wishes to demonstrate or observe.

There is no need to damage a mature productive colony, or spend valuable time sorting through twenty combs for the queen and suitable combs, if the stocking process is undertaken from nuclei. These do present snags and an extra stage but in many ways they are far easier to handle.

Choice of bees and combs   The normal two or three frame uni-comb observation hive is one of the most artificial methods of management under which honeybees can be kept, but of all systems of beekeeping, the observation hive is the one which gives the non-beekeeper the most frequent opportunities to examine the comb on which the bees live. Prior to their installation the bees will have been subject to a series of preparatory manipulations and if the hive is kept occupied for some time they may well need additional manipulations. It should be borne in mind that any outbreak of disease, as well as disrupting the work programme of experiments and observation, will also present problems of disinfection of the hive and combs.

Four basic factors will therefore influence the choice of bees and combs for use in the observation hive:

(1) Freedom from brood and adult diseases, and parasites.
(2) Hardiness and economy in the use of stores.
(3) Docility.
(4) Clean comb with a range of stores and cell patterns.

Freedom from disease and parasites   One of the most embarrassing things that can happen to the owner of an observation hive is to have it placed on public display and then be told that the brood or the adults exhibit one or other of the bee diseases or parasites. Adult disease, dysentery apart, is less likely to attract the layman's attention, although too many bees with the 'K' wing symptom of acarine will draw unfavourable comment from other beekeepers. Under the adverse conditions in the average observation hive disease can rapidly reduce a once thriving colony to an ineffective group of bees, invalidating any experimental or observation work being undertaken. Although all hives are liable to pick up disease, in the establishment of the observation hive every care should be taken to ensure that the source of the bees is free of known disease or parasites.

Hardiness If the colony is to be maintained for more than a few days, one is faced with a number of problems arising from the ability of the bees to survive in what, for them, are very confined and inhospitable quarters. The tall, thin nesting area is difficult to heat in cold weather, and equally difficult to cool in hot weather. In all conditions it is difficult to ventilate and when sealed stores are being used in any quantity condensation can become a problem which the bees find it difficult to overcome.

It is clear that some colonies survive better than others in observation hives so that once a source of 'good survivors' has been located, every care should be taken to preserve them. Prolific breeding or heavy use of stores will also count against a colony, but it is also true that under unnatural conditions some queens fail to produce sufficient brood to maintain even a small colony.

Docility If the selection of comb, stores and brood is to be given the attention it deserves, then the stocking of the observation hive is preceded by a series of manipulations involving the preparation of nuclei and the selection of suitable combs. If care is not taken to choose docile bees this selection process can be made unpleasant if not impossible; under these circumstances it is often wiser to abandon working with a particular stock. During the lifetime of a long-term observation hive it may be desirable to open the hive and exchange combs; this, too, is made easier with good tempered bees.

Suitability of comb It is usual to prepare an observation hive knowing that at some point in its life it will be placed on public view. It is therefore desirable that the comb should be reasonably new, not old, brown or spotted with dysenteric droppings. Members of the public are unlikely to purchase honey if they see stores and nectar in ancient, dirty comb.

In the chapter on judging observation hives it is suggested that the desirable condition to be aimed at is a hive so arranged that it presents a cross-section through a normal colony and does not look too much like a set of adjacent combs placed one above the other on the day before the show. Combs should be selected to exhibit a range of comb structure; worker cells, drone cells, and transition cells between the

22. Single frame observation hive, Czechoslovakia 1963.

two. It should not be forgotten that bees normally keep their stores in deeper cells than those in which they raise their brood, and a progression from deep to normal cells should be looked for.

When a colony is subject to a steady nectar flow, rope-like clusters of wax secreting bees will form, although they will hardly be visible if confined to the space between the frames. When, however, a small section of comb is cut out, the bees will soon gather to take advantage of the space thus provided and their system of working with wax will be visible.

23. Hive with both brood body and observation section, Czechoslovakia 1963.

Preparing the nucleus   Whatever our objective, the safest way to stock the observation hive is to prepare one or more nuclei either by drawing combs from a number of colonies in the apiary or by designating a mother colony. In either case we shall need an adequate supply of used new comb, fresh comb being too frail for use in the avarage observation hive. There are then three alternatives:

(1) the nucleus can be allowed to raise its own queen prior to transfer to the observation hive,

(2) the bees may raise a queen in the observation hive,

(3) a queen from the main apiary can be given to spend her final season or two heading the small colony in the observation hive.

Preparing nuclei from a number of colonies may be practised as part of the main apiary swarm control system but it does add a further complication to the preliminary work. On the other hand, earmarking and the selection of a mother colony which will not be worked for honey or taken for pollination will simplify the process.

A single brood-chamber mother colony can be kept well fed so that it is able to maintain a high level of brood production as well as lay down adequate stores in the upper part of the brood nest. It is important to have a young queen capable of a steady level of egg production. Regular removal of the original combs and then those of the current season will contain the colony, without difficulty, within one brood box. A regular supply of new comb or frames fitted with foundation will be required. It is preferable to have new frames although old frames which have been well cleaned and scraped can be used.

The final transfer   Having established a nucleus, it must then be decided whether the observation hive is to be stocked *in situ* or dismounted and taken to the site of the nucleus. Under certain circumstances it is possible to bring the nucleus to the observation hive, let the bees settle down for a day or two to get accustomed to the location of the new site, and then to carry out the transfer. On the other hand, it may be safer in a busy place to dismount the hive and transport it to the apiary where the transfer can be conducted without risk of stings to non-beekeepers.

It is at this stage that the beekeeper can make the final selection of comb and determine the initial amounts of brood, stores and bees. It is to be expected that a normal two or three frame observation hive will be made up from a four frame nucleus and provision should therefore be made to house the surplus combs. If more than one hive is to be stocked then it is possible to form an additional nucleus from the remaining frames. It is always a good precaution to have a spare queen or queen cell to hand for this purpose or in case a selected queen gets lost or damaged.

Adequate stores of honey or nectar and pollen should be available in the observation hive in case bad weather overtakes the small colony in its establishment stage; also for use before the bees locate good sources of food, or if they remain confined in the hive for some days.

In transferring the combs to the hive it is essential that the queen is found and her position on the comb noted. Care should be taken to ensure that she does not fall from the frame during transfer or is crushed when the hive is closed.

Care of the observation hive   The stocking of an observation hive lays a special responsibility on the beekeeper. Most colonies of bees will not need the regular detailed attention required by other livestock, but once confined in an observation hive the small colony becomes extremely vulnerable to external influences.

In hot weather the tall, thin hive is difficult to cool; failure to close a sun blind or draw a curtain may cause severe distress or even destroy a colony if it is exposed to full sun. On the other hand, in cold weather an open door or window admitting a sharp draught can render part of the hive uninhabitable and result in the death or stunting of the brood.

A few days wet or cold weather can reduce a colony to starvation. A two frame hive will consume over 450 cc of strong sugar syrup per day and although it will not require weekend attention, no hive should be left unattended for more than three days. Under conditions of good nectar flow it is possible to find most cells filled with honey and/or nectar and it is then advisable to replace one or more combs.

In early spring, when sealed stores are being used, considerable condensation will form in the hive which may then need opening for the vents to be cleaned. At this time of the year, cold quite often prevents the cleaning bees from removing rubbish or dead bees from the entrance tube, which becomes clogged. The colony is then held prisoner behind a barrier of its own dead bodies.

During feeding, observation hives are attractive to other colonies so that robbing should be guarded against. Symptoms of adult and brood diseases should be watched for at all times as well as insect parasites of the comb and bees.

To maintain a good observation hive is a severe test of a beekeeper's skill.

CHAPTER SIX

EXHIBITING AND JUDGING

From the establishment of honey shows in the eighteen hundred and seventies until the middle years of the present century, stocked observation hives featured in many British local and national exhibitions of bees and beekeeping. The purpose of these hives was both to attract and educate the general public and to form part of competitive displays between one beekeeper and another. However, since the Second World War this type of competition has largely died out. In part this may be due to the fact that observation hives are no longer a feature of the National Honey Show, London, which is now held in October—a time of year when it would be extremely difficult to prepare and maintain exhibition observation hives. It is also true that growing interest in the welfare of wild life leads associations to insist that bees in observation hives have access to an open flight area if they are to be confined for more than one day. This requirement limits the staging of observation hives to one day shows or to tents and halls from which it is possible to construct entrance tubes for the hives.

Herrod-Hempsall (1948) in his book *Preparing, exhibiting and judging bee produce* summarized the rules for judging observation hives with a basic proviso that the construction of the hive should be such that the sacrifice of bee life is avoided. He also established a five point judging code:

1. The colony should be free of observable disease, with special reference to brood diseases.

71

2. The hive should be properly ventilated.
3. A store of food should be present in the cells, both pollen and honey as well as nectar or sugar syrup.
4. Adult bees of all three castes should be present.
5. Drone, worker and queen cells should be present, the first two occupied by eggs and larvae, the queen cell either occupied or recently vacated by a queen.

In the period between staging the hive and the judging, the exhibitor or show steward should remove one shutter from the hive so that the queen, who will tend to move away from the light, will make for the covered comb surface and so be quickly found by the judge when he removes the second shutter.

It is strange that Herrod-Hempsall, who so often went into great detail on other beekeeping matters, should not have made the point that an exhibition observation hive, in addition to its brood, stores and bees drawn from the different castes, should also represent a vertical cross-section through a hive. In most observation hives it is clear that the combs have been selected from a horizontal brood nest and re-arranged vertically by the beekeeper. It is a council of perfection to suggest that the combs should be drawn from a double brood-chamber hive to show the brood area surrounded by an upper layer of sealed stores with an arch of raw nectar and pollen below.

The normal honeybee colony, if space allows, constructs a tall, thin nest with the honey stores separated from the brood by an arch of pollen-filled cells; observation hives should exhibit this characteristic. It is not sufficient to go to a hive the day before the exhibition, extract comb from a single brood box and hope that the bees will make the required rearrangement overnight.

The comb in an exhibition observation hive should be sound and clean, not old, damaged or discoloured. In a three comb hive at least part of one comb should be cut away so that the bees can be induced to demonstrate the wax secretion comb construction phase of colony life. The use of coloured foundation will also demonstrate the process of wax recycling. Bees will draw out the lower walls of the cells from the wax of coloured foundation before incorporating any new, white wax of their own secretion. A brick red sheet of foundation will produce

Fig. 8. Modern bee house and swarmgatherer c. 1794. From K. A. Forster, Zurich *Die Biene*.

red, then pink, cell walls with softly tinted capping to complete the work.

The preparation of an exhibition observation hive should be seen as a step-by-step process, working from a selected single chamber colony housed on new comb, with four combs chosen to form a nucleus from which the observation hive is finally made up. In this way no colony selected for honey production is damaged and the beekeeper has only a relatively few bees to work with when stocking the observation hive. An outcome of the stocking process will be one or more nuclei in which young queens are raised and held, and who, if not required for observation hives, can be used to head new productive colonies in the following year.

CHAPTER SEVEN

SOME EQUIPMENT SUPPLY HOUSES AND THEIR ADDRESSES

EQUIPMENT AND BOOKS

AUSTRIA
Franz Schade, KG, Kunstoff-Spritzerei, 1150 WIEN 15, Henriettenplatz, Austria
CANADA
Hodgson Bee Supplies Ltd, 7925-13th Avenue, P.O. Box 297, New Westminster, BC
FRANCE
Ets d'Apiculture Trubert, 38 rue du Faubourg La Grappe, 28000 Chartres
Ets Thomas Fils, Boite Postale no. 2, 45450 Fay-au-Loges
GERMAN FEDERAL REPUBLIC
Hammann, 6733 Hassloch Pfalz, Postf. 225
Chr. Graze KG, 7056 Weinstadt-Endersbach, bei Stuttgart, Postf. 2107
Eugen Herzog, D-723 Schramberg 1, Postf. 146
IRISH REPUBLIC
John Atkins & Co. Ltd, 4–5 Winthrop St, Cork
Irish Agricultural Wholesale Society Ltd, 151–156 Thomas St, Dublin 8 Telephone 717131
P. J. Keating, Skeeter Park, Bargy Commons, Murrintown, Co. Wexford.

UNITED KINGDOM
Robert Lee (Bee Supplies) Ltd, Beehive Works, George St, Uxbridge, Middlesex UB8 1SX. *Telephone* 0895 33181
Mountain Grey Apiaries, Holme-on-Spalding Moor, York YO4 4EZ. *Telephone* 069 63 338
R. Steel & Brodie, Bee Hive Works, Wormit, Fife DD6 8PG. *Telephone* 082 66 728
E. H. Taylor Ltd, Welwyn, Herts AL6 0AZ. *Telephone* 043 871 4401
E. H. Thorne (Beehives) Ltd, Beehive Works, Wragby, Lincoln LN3 5LA. *Telephone* 067 34 555
Woodland Apiaries Ltd, Manor Farm, Farthingstone, Nr Towcester NN12 8EZ. *Telephone* 032 736 237
UNITED STATES
Dadant & Sons Inc., Hamilton, IL 62341
A. I. Root Company, Medina, OH 44256
Walter T. Kelley Co., Clarkson, KY 42726

SPECIALIST BOOK FIRMS

Bee Books New & Old, Jasmin Cottage, Steventon, Nr Basingstoke, Hants
Northern Bee Books, Scout Bottom Farm, Mytholmroyd, Halifax, W. Yorks

CHAPTER EIGHT

BIBLIOGRAPHY

In selecting material for this bibliography I have been guided by the wish to provide a useful list of relevant publications. Although most books on the art of beekeeping include a passing reference to the observation hive, these generally add little to the subject so I have excluded reference to them.

In Britain local public libraries are now connected to the national British Library system and can obtain items fairly quickly from libraries elsewhere in the country. In other countries similar systems operate. Those with access to college or university libraries should also find little difficulty in arranging inter library loans. Members of the International Bee Research Association are able to borrow the originals or purchase photocopies. Because this Bibliography has been built up out of two groups of material available in the Association library, it is made up of two different references:

(1) Items published before the abstract journal *Apicultural Abstracts* commenced publication in 1950. These have no prefix number e.g. BEVAN, E. (1870).

(2) The titles of items included in *Apicultural Abstracts* are prefixed by the abstract reference number and the year of publication e.g. 119/51 (item number 119 in the 1951 volume). Items including an L in the distinguishing number 816L/76 are included with title only.

References are listed in alphabetical order of author(s). Publications are in English, except where otherwise indicated, e.g. *In Russian*. An English translation of the title is added in these cases.

119/51 ALLERTON, J. T., Shirley, Birmingham, Great Britain
Good Beekeeping, 6(1): 8–10 (1951)
The new observation frame

'Down the cell' observation of bees at work may lead to incorrect conclusions. A longitudinal section of cells gives much greater scope, enabling the observer to see the storing of honey and pollen, the laying of eggs, the feeding of larvae, etc.

The author describes and illustrates the construction of a frame which exposes to view a large number of longitudinal sections of cells, and which is interchangeable with an ordinary frame.

15/54 APPEL, H., Werste bei Bad Oeynhausen, Germany
Leipzig, Bienenztg. (West) 65*(8): 240–243 (1951) *In German*
In praise of the observation hive

The author has had an observation hive on his window sill for 30 years; the colony became queenless only twice during that time, and swarmed regularly between the 5th and 12th of May (the stock was thus requeened); alternatively the two brood combs were replaced by foundation and used for strengthening weak colonies in the apiary. There is an interesting account of educational value of an observation hive.

*[given as 66]

BEVAN, E.
London: Van Voorst 384 pages + 21 plates rev. ed. (1870)
The honeybee, its natural history, physiology and management

BOYKIN, M. N. (1953)
Glean in Bee Cult. 81(5): 280–281 (1953)
My observation bee hive
239/52 CHAUVIN, R., Station de recherches apicoles, Bures-sur-Yvette (S.-et-O), France
Apiculteur 94(11) *Sect. sci.* No 4: 57–68 (1950) *In French*
Method of uninterrupted observation of the laying of a queen bee

Foundation was attached to one side of sheets of glass; it was drawn out by the bees and they obligingly removed the wax from the bottom of the cells, so that the eggs were deposited on the glass. Observations were made daily from May 21 to July 31 with two of these combs in a hive, one above the other.

Pollen. Cells with pollen were counted every day, but it was impossible to see the depth of pollen in each cell. At first it was placed in the middle of the upper half comb on the left, where laying started; later it was removed and put lower down. The behaviour of the pollen-carrying bees was erratic: they moved about the comb, now and then performing their characteristic dance, and suddenly deposited the pollen in cells and immediately departed, leaving other bees to do the packing.

Nectar. The behaviour of bees was even more erratic than with pollen, but it was generally deposited outside the brood. It was difficult to see, being transparent.

Eggs and brood. A grid of white thread was used on the glass to facilitate counting. The number of eggs laid each day varied from 1100 to 0; usually it was 300–400. The queen laid in a vaguely concentric way. When there was a shortage of nectar the eggs were frequently removed, particularly from the edges of the brood nest.

The queen. She always remained on the brood; even when the upper comb was full and the bottom one—although well covered by bees—practically empty, the queen did not go there. As soon as capping of the brood started, the queen reduced her laying. The author believes that this is normal and not due to the special hive.

Laying cycle. There were 3 maxima: 1 (June 2) 1697 eggs in the combs; 2 (June 28) 1311 eggs; 3 (July 14) 779 eggs. The maximum numbers of pupae were: 1 (June 20) 4896; 2 (July 12) 3575; 3 (July 31) 1377. The author believes that these cycles of laying are normal and, within certain limits, independent of outside influence. He suggests also that nurses reared later may not be as good as those reared earlier.

329/69 DOUAULT, P., Station de Recherches sur l'Abeille, Bures sur-Yvette (S. & O.), France
Annls Abeille 11(1): 63–67 (1968) *In French: English summary*

Description and utilization of two types of small experimental hives containing one or two combs

These wooden hives were designed for use in behavioural studies. They have Plexiglas windows, with circular openings for manipulation and are equipped with a heating system.

816L/76 DOUAULT, P.
Cahiers de Liaison OPIE (1974) No. 13, 22–27 *In French.*
Laboratory (observation) hives

1207/77 FREE, J. B.; WILLIAMS, I. H. Rothamsted Exp. Stn., Harpenden, Herts., UK.

Applied Animal Ethology (1976) 2, 141–154

The effect on the foraging behaviour of honeybees of the relative locations of the hive entrance and brood combs.

Hives consisted of a tier of 11-frame chambers and were provided with upper and lower entrances. Observations within hives were made via a glass floorboard. When a hive entrance opened directly on to the brood area of a colony, a greater proportion of bees using it collected pollen than when it opened on to an area of the hive with storage comb only, and the proportion of pollen gatherers could be diminished or increased by moving brood combs near to or far from the entrance. Relatively more bees left than entered by an entrance near the brood, particularly when the brood was adjacent to the lower entrance.

On return from foraging, bees tended to remain faithful to one entrance only, but the presence of a queen excluder obstructed the movement of foragers within the hives and, as a consequence, there was a greater tendency for the bees to change entrances in accordance with a change in the position of the brood.

By manipulating the size and shape of the hive entrance it was possible to direct returning foragers to the brood combs, and hence to increase their tendency to collect pollen and thus their pollinating efficiency.

FRISCH, K. VON. University of Munich

Cambridge, Mass.: Harvard University Press (1967) 566 pp.

The dance language and orientation of bees

905/73 GALE, F. C. San Jose State Coll. San Jose, CA, USA

American Bee Journal (1972) 112 (1) 8–9

Observation beehives

Two different types of glass-walled hives are described. One is a permanent classroom type and has 4 tiers each for 2 combs side by side. The central standard-depth frames are fitted with a special 'right angle comb holder', next to an extra pane of glass, which prevents attachment of the combs to the outer glass, and this unit can be replaced with standard frames. Sliding masonite covers with nichrome wire grids, giving thermostatic control, serve to heat the hive.

The other type is a portable single-frame hive, in which both the glass pane and masonite cover on each side can be easily removed. A luggage-type handle in the centre of the top serves for carrying. Two screened holes at each end provide ventilation. Both hives have provision for a feeding jar and access to the outside to allow foraging.

227L/77 GARY, N. & LORENZEN, K. University of California Cooperative Extension
Leaflet, Cooperative Extension, University of California (1976) No. 2853, 20 pp.
How to construct and maintain an observation bee hive

224/58 GILLARD, A. & LAERE, O. VAN, Institut agronomique de l'Etat, Gand, Belgium
Rev. Agric., Brux. 10(2): 231–236 (1957) *In French*
Construction of a perspex observation hive

Clear instructions and diagrams are given to enable the reader to construct this hive, which is made entirely of perspex with the exception of the floor board. The perspex is glued together with a special adhesive. The author suggests placing the frames too close together for the bees to pass between them, so that they remain in sight. He has various other tips for getting the greatest interest and enjoyment out of the hive.

432L/74 GOJMURAC, W. L., University of Wisconsin—Extension
Fact Sheet, University of Wisconsin—Extension (1973) No. A2491, 4 pp.
Reprinted in *American Bee Journal* 113(9) 332–334 (1973)
Building and operating an observation beehive

GUY, R. (1970)
S. A. Bee J. 42(6): 6–9 (1970)
A simple observation hive

HERROD-HEMPSALL, W. (1930)
London: *British Bee Journal* Vol. 1: 1–772 (1930), Vol. II: 773–1842 (1937)
Beekeeping new and old described with pen and camera

267/61 KHALIFMAN, I. A., Agrobiologiya, Orlikov per 1/11, Moscow, USSR
Moskva: Izdutel'stvo 'Sovetskaya Rossiya' 55 pages (1960) *In Russian*
The observation hive

This booklet gives a popular history of observation hives from ancient times, referring to the works of Rychhov, Huber, Prokopovich, Kondrat'ev, Perepelova, Gubin, von Frisch, and others. An account is given of the methods by which simple observations can be conducted with observation hives, and of different types of these hives.

The Russian adjective *primechatel'nyi* used in the title can be interpreted as remarkable, or impressive and at the same time allowing observations. P. I. Rychkov, author of the first original work in Russian on beekeeping [1767], called his hive *primechatel'nyi*.

431L/74 KOLB, H., Edmond, Oklahoma, USA, (1974) 4 pp
Observation beehive: approved classroom model; standard small-colony shipping cage

731/72 LAERE, O. VAN, Station d'Entemologie de l'Etat, Oosterzelesteenweg 86, Vantegem-Wetteren, Belgium
Apidologie 2(1): 111–116 (1971) *In French: English & German summaries*
Construction of two types of experimental hive

Two types of experimental hives are described and illustrated: the first can house 2000–5000 bees for an indefinite period, and may be fitted with 1, 2 or 3 Dadant frames: the second is designed to house 50–200 bees, with or without queens, for a couple of weeks in controlled environmental conditions.

LANGSTROTH, L. L. (1857)
New York: C. N. Saxton & Co. 534 pages, 2nd ed. (1857), rp. Root (1978)
A practical treatise on the hive and honey-bee

684/66 LEHNERT, T. & CANTWELL, G. E., USDA Bee Disease Investigations Lab., Beltsville, Md. 20705, USA
Am. Bee J. 106(9): 336–337 (1966)
The Beltsville research apiarium

This building (3.3 × 5.4 m) houses about 25 three-frame observation hives, whose adjacent external entrances are painted in different colours and designs. Hives are made of aluminium and easily heat-sterilized. Tests with biological insecticides showed that *Bacillus thuringiensis* (spore, crystal, and exotoxin fractions), and several insect viruses at concentrations used for pest control, were not harmful to honeybees.

59/61 LEITGEB, R. Universitätsstrasse 13, Innsbruck, Austria
Alpendland, Bienenztg (7): 237–242 (1958) *In German*
A two-frame hive

A two-frame hive, with glass walls but well insulated, is described with constructional diagrams. It is used for making a nucleus, its advantage being that it can be inspected easily. Details of the author's queen-rearing method are given.

NEIGHBOUR, A.
London: Kent 354 pages 3rd ed. (1878)
The apiary; or, bees, beehives, and bee culture

NUTT, T.
Wisbech: Published by the author 240 pages (1832)
Humanity to honey bees ...

817L/76 OHIO STATE UNIVERSITY COOPERATIVE EXTENSION SERVICE
Beekeeping Information, Cooperative Extension Service, Ohio State University
(1974) No. 10, 4 pp.
Observation bee hives

PETTITT, W. J.
Dover, UK; printed by W. Brett ii + 50 pp. 2nd and enlarged edition (1867)
The management of bees ... with a catalogue of hives and apiarian furniture

ROBB, D.
Scot. Beekpr 27(11): 216–217 (1951)
The 'Robb' cross-sectional observation hive

152/70 ROTHENBUHLER, W. C., THOMPSON, N. C., & McDERMOTT, J. J., Zoology Dept. Ohio State Uni., Columbus, USA
J. apic. Res., 7(3): 151–155 (1968)
Control of the environment of honeybee observation colonies by the use of hive-shelters and flight-cages

Descriptions are given of observation hives, a portable building to house the hives, and cages to confined flight of the colonies under observation. The building contains a thermostatically controlled exhaust fan and heater to provide a warm environment for the small colonies.

128/51 RUTTNER, F., Bienenabteilung, Biologischen Station, Lunz, Austria
Wetter und Leben 2(9–10): 211–214 (1950) *In German*
The life of the colony as shown by a self-recording balance

A continuous and permanent record of hive weight is recommended as being far more useful than the isolated figures obtained from the usual scale hive. At Lunz an ordinary colony balance is used, but its turning-point is damped with a spring so that its amplitude corresponds to several kg.; the position is recorded on a rotating drum by a stylo.

Two graphs, one for two consecutive sunny July days and one for a cloudy July day, show solar radiation (in cal./cm.^{2}) and weight plotted against time. The first graph shows how after a slight but continuous decline during the night (due to the consumption of food and loss of water in ripening honey), the hive weight dropped suddenly as the sunlight increased and the bees left, reaching a minimum round noon. During the afternoon the weight increased steadily as nectar and pollen were carried in, and then sharply in the evening as the field bees returned. The second graph shows a similar decline during the night which steepened as the bees flew out in the morning, but there are two distinct maxima showing how the foragers returned when the sky clouded over.

217/56 RYCKMAN, R. E., Coll. Medical Evangelists, Loma Linda, Calif, USA
J. econ. Ent. 48(6): 755–756 (1955)
Potentialities of the otoscope in entomological research

The author used this physician's instrument [otoscope or auriscope] with advantage to observe honeybee larvae in a glass-walled hive. It pin-points

a light of adjustable intensity into small recesses and provides a 2.35×
magnifying lens.

60/68 SAKAGAMI, S. F., Zoological Inst., Hokkaido Univ., Sapporo-Shi,
Japan
Papéis Dept. Zool. S. Paulo 19: 151–162 (1966) *In English*
**Techniques for the observation of behaviour and social organiza-
tion of stingless bees by using a special hive**

Constructional details are provided for an improved version of Kerr's
observation hive [see *A.A.* 270/67]. Some 19 species belonging to 8 genera
have been reared in the hive, and some results have already been published
[*A.A.* 40/67].

181/58 SCHÖNMANN, W. & JOSS, H., Switzerland
Berne: Paul Haupt 56 pages (1957) *In German*
We ask the bees: observations and experiments for nature lovers

Review: This attractive little book is designed to introduce teachers and
nature lovers to experimental observation of bee behaviour. The first section,
for which it is not necessary to have access to a colony of bees, deals with
marking bees and training them in the field to use artificial feeding places,
with details of experiments to test the bee's senses of smell, taste and colour
vision.

The second section gives constructional details of an observation hive,
with notes on the behaviour of the queen and or the several functions of
the workers and their dances. The third section describes the dissection of
the bee's legs, wings, mouthparts, sting, *etc.*, for microscopical examination,
and the making of models to demonstrate the action of the legs and wings.

The book is practical, up to date, and illustrated with clear drawings.

SHAW, F. R.
Glean: Bee Cult. 80(11): 656–658 (1952)
Observation beehives: construction—use

243/53 SHAW, F. R., University of Massachusetts, Amherst, Mass., USA
Spec. Circ. Mass. Ext. Serv. No. 191: 2 pages (1952)
Ruches d'observation/Beobachtungs-bienenkasten
Observation beehives

Construction and suggestions are given for use of observation hives in
teaching.

SHULL, J. H.
Glean: Bee Cult. 78(12): 28–730 (1950)
An observation beehive

VOLCINSCHI, T.
Apicultura, Bucuresti 25(2): 23–26 (1972) *In Rumanian*
The observation hive

Index

Only the supply houses *and persons* cited in the main text are included in this index. A detailed list of some equipment supply houses and specialist book firms will be found in Chapter Seven; Chapter Eight forms a bibliography, with some annotations.